by Mike Thaler

SCHOLASTIC BOOK SERVICES
NEW YORK • TORONTO • LONDON • AUCKLAND • SYDNEY • TOKYO

For Sam and Lilian

 Published by Scholastic Book Services, a division of Scholastic Magazines, Inc.

1st printing .... December 1974

Printed in the U.S.A.

HI

How do you make **MICE** cold?

Take away the **M** and they turn into **ICE**.

What letter will make a **COOK** dishonest?

An **R** will make a
COOK a **CROOK**.

How do you make a **CHAIR** disappear?

Take away **CH** and the **CHAIR** becomes **AIR**.

How do you make a
WITCH scratch?

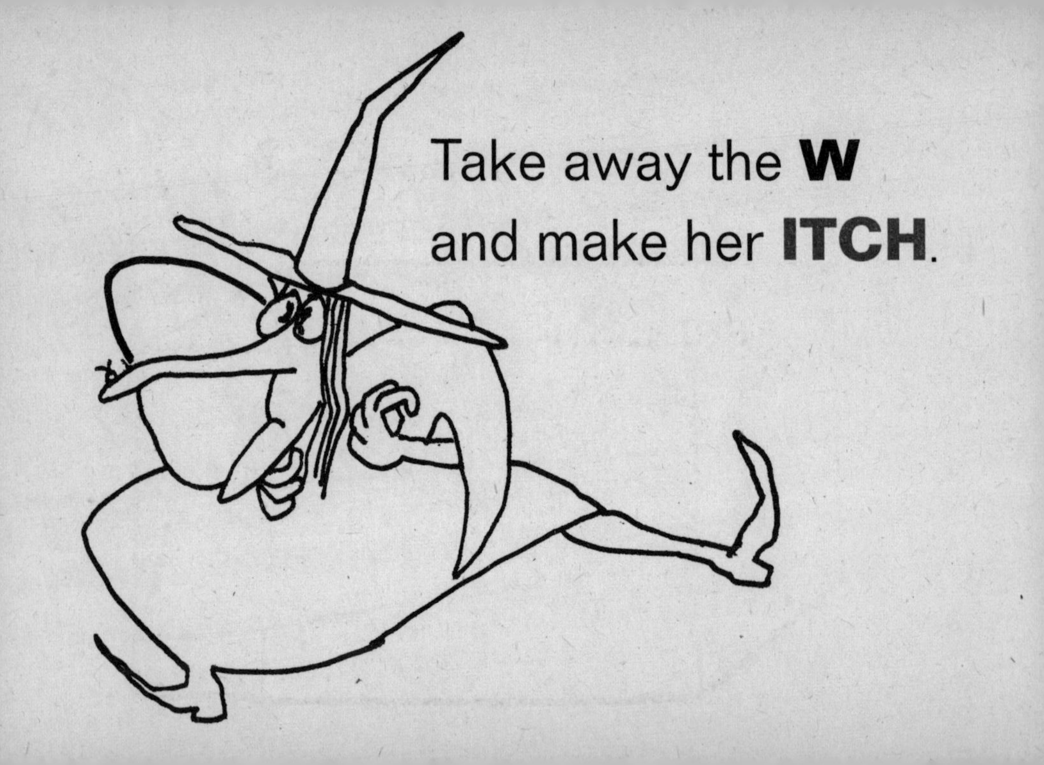

Take away the **W**
and make her **ITCH**.

What animal is in **BOX**?

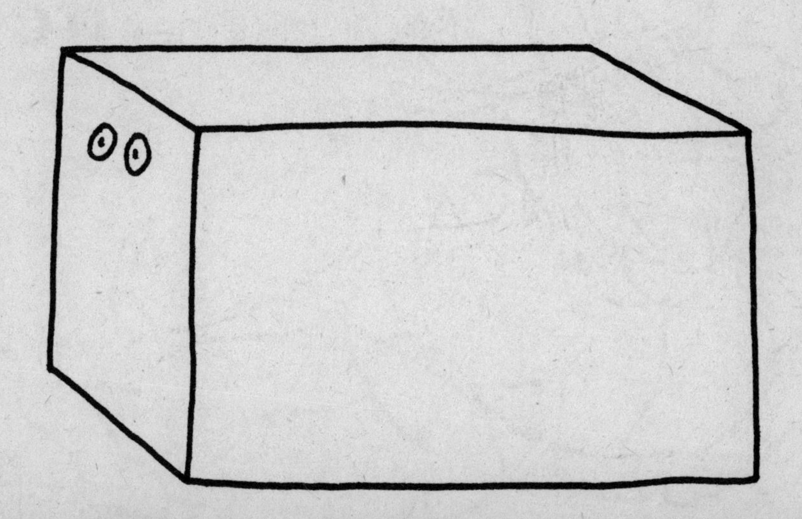

OX.

How do you make a **BRUSH** go faster?

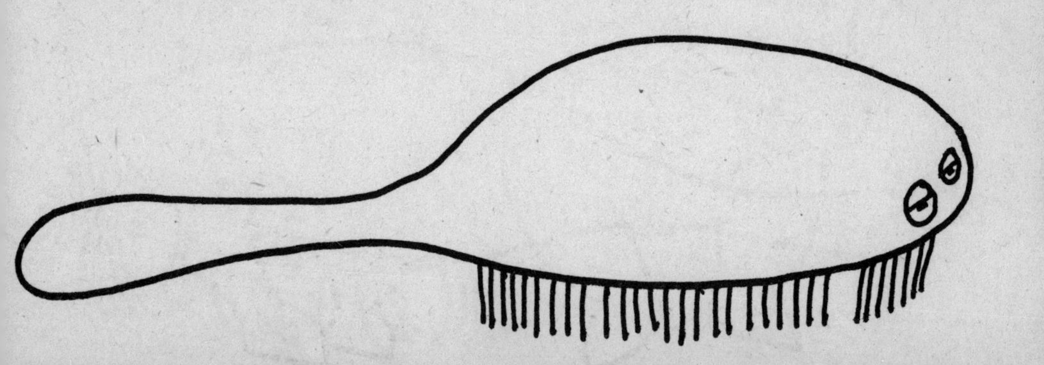

Take away its **B** and make it **RUSH**.

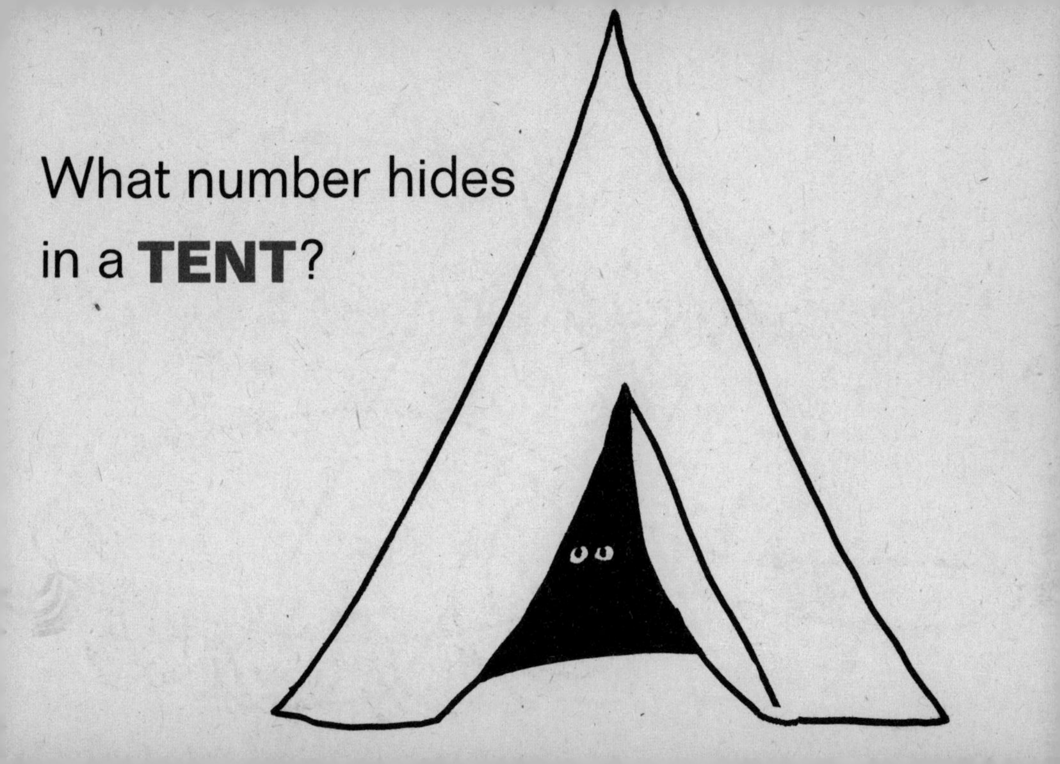
What number hides
in a TENT?

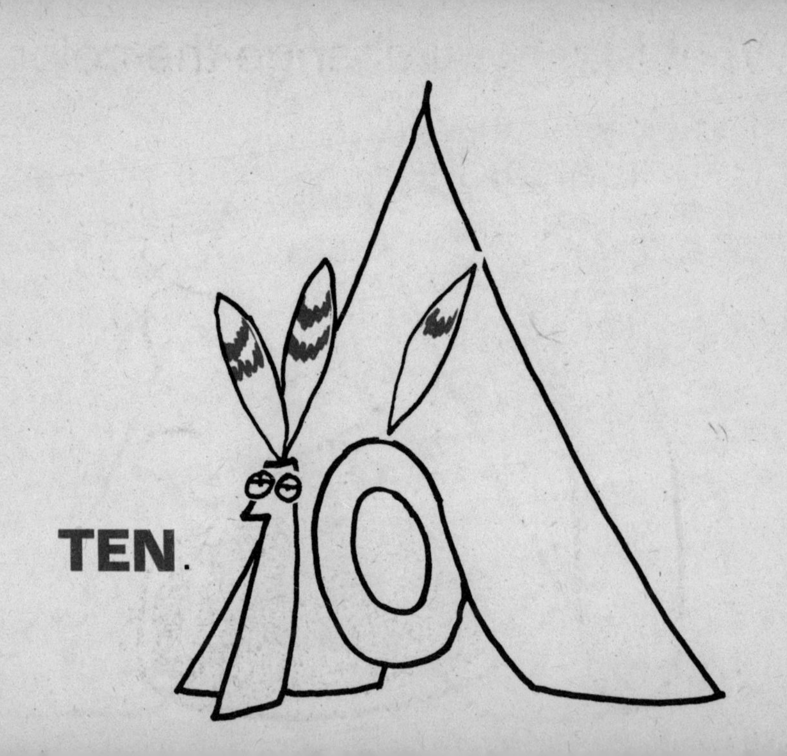
TEN.

What letter will change the color of **INK**?

P will make it **PINK**.

What animal hides in a **GRAPE**?

An **APE**.

How can you make a GIANT small?
WHY DON'T YOU PICK ON SOMEONE YOUR OWN SIZE?

Take away his **GI** and make him an **ANT**.

How can you make a
CART go faster?

Take away its **T** and make it a **CAR**.

What does a **COUCH** say if you pinch its **C**?

OUCH!
C

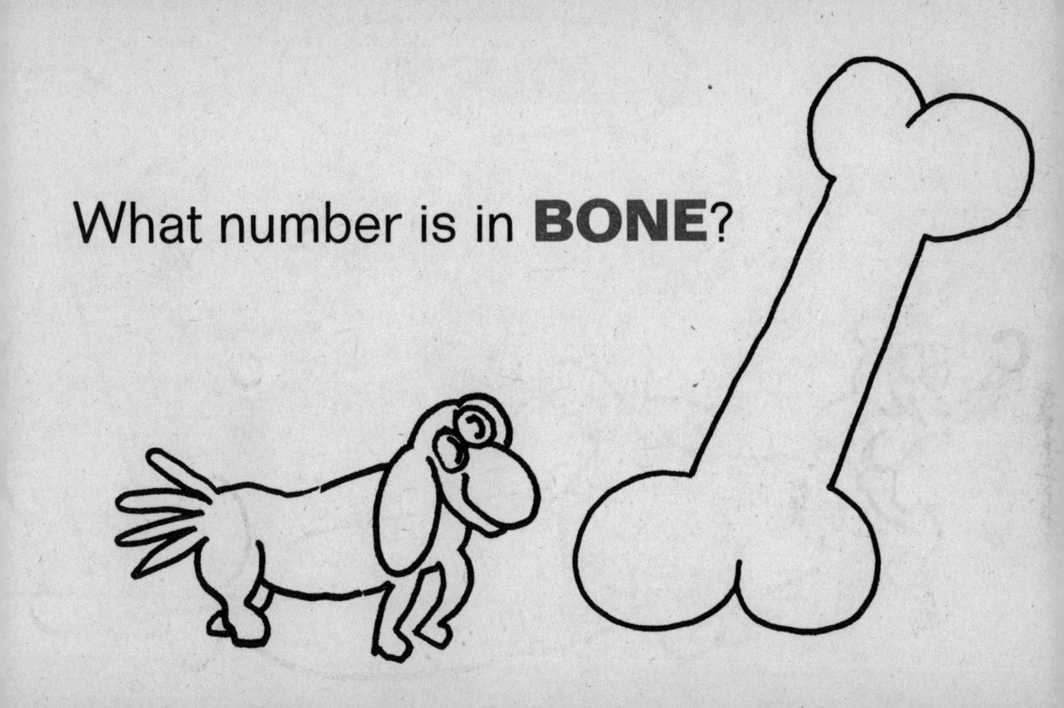
What number is in **BONE**?

ONE.

How can you make a **BEAGLE** fly?

Take away his **B** and
make him an **EAGLE**.

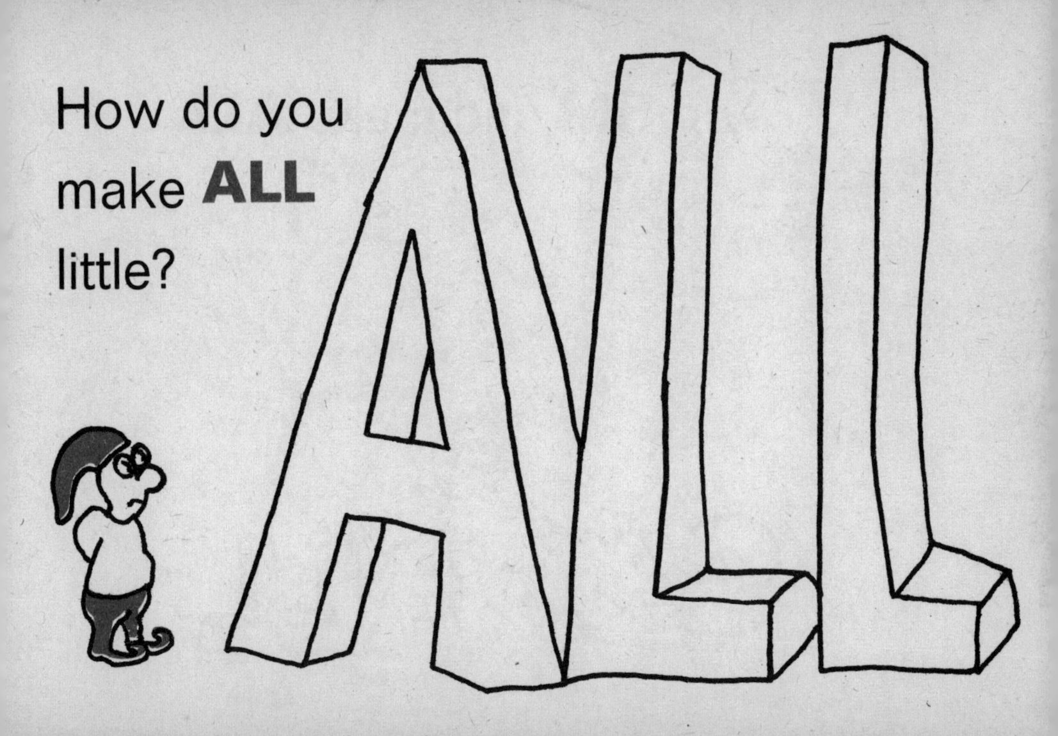
How do you make **ALL** little?
ALL

Add **SM** and make **ALL**

SMALL.

How do you make **ALL** bigger?

Add a T
and make
ALL TALL.
TALL

What letter will chase away a **CAT**?

S will make it **SCAT**.

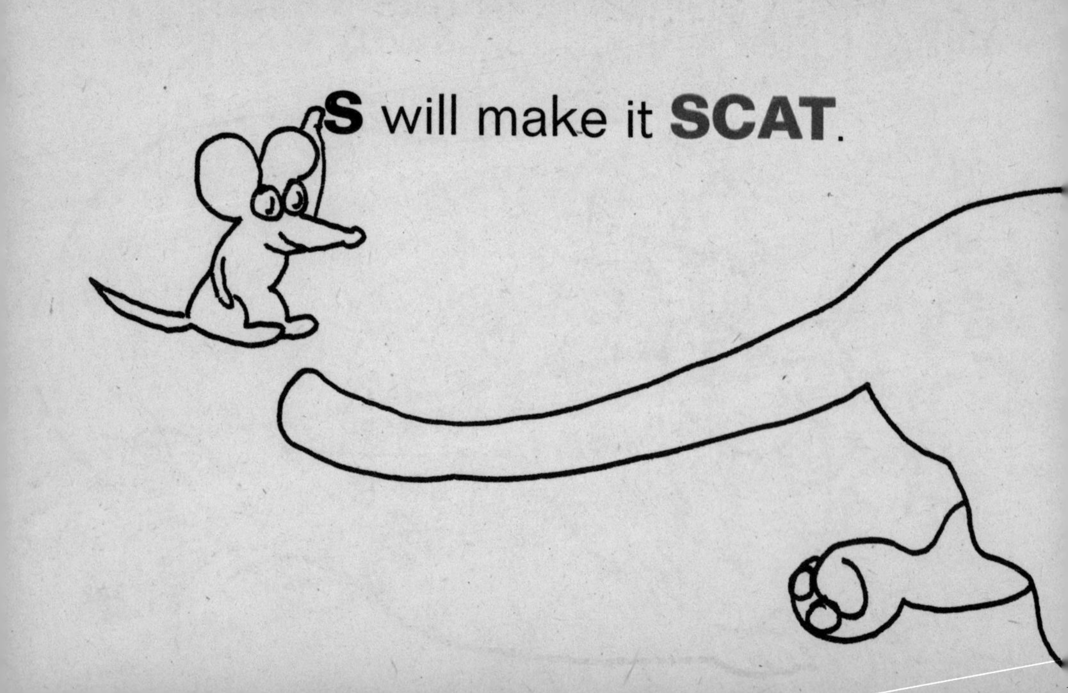

What animal is in this **FOX**?

An **OX**.

What animal is in this **BATH**?

A **BAT**.

What letter will dress **ANTS**?

P will dress **ANTS** in **PANTS**.

What letter will make **CREAM** loud?

An **S** will make **CREAM**

What's the sweetest thing you can make from **MONEY**?

HONEY.

What can a **COOK**
make with a **Y**?

A **COOKY**.

How can you make a **CLOWN** feel like a king?

Change L into R and
give him a CROWN.

What letter can you take away to make a **SNAIL** go faster?

Take away his **N** and make him **SAIL**.

What letter will make **EARS** cry?

T will turn **EARS** to **TEARS**.

What letter will make a **PLUM** fatter?

P will make a **PLUM PLUMP**.

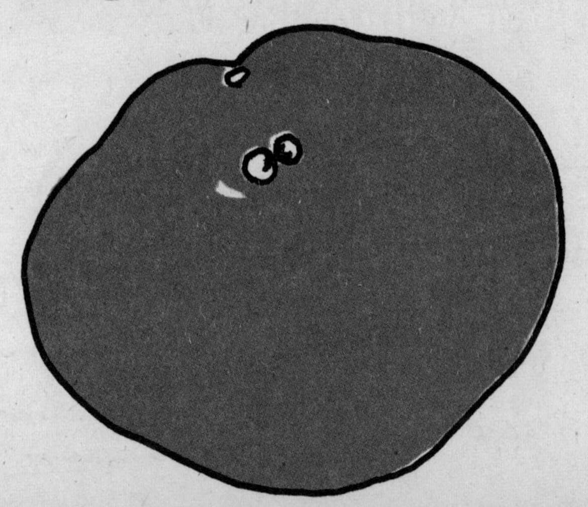

What letter will make a **HAT** talk?

A **C** will make a **HAT CHAT**.

What little creature can you find in a **SHELF**?

An **ELF**.
BYE

NOW DO SOME MAGIC LETTER RIDDLES OF YOUR OWN!

ABOUT THE AUTHOR

Mike Thaler, who wrote and illustrated this book, is the creator of the popular *Letterman* series for THE ELECTRIC COMPANY on National Educational Television. When he is not busy writing (he has written 13 children's books), Mr. Thaler is a sculptor, a draftsman and a cartoonist whose work has appeared in major magazines. A native Californian, Mr. Thaler now makes his home in Roundout Valley, New York, where he teaches story-making to fourth graders and takes an active part in community affairs.